THE BEAVER ANNUAL

EDITED BY

NANCY SPAIN

WITH

ILLUSTRATIONS BY W. S. GREENHALGH

Contents

**edited by
NANCY SPAIN**

illustrations by
W.S.GREENHALGH

6

FINALLY, MUCH LATER...

SO...

The End

so you want to be a NURSE by Gwen Jarran

ASK any nurse and she will tell you she wouldn't change her chosen career for the world. Yes, it's hard work being a nurse, and there's discipline too. But the satisfactions are very great. It is a fine thing to feel that you are helping others at a time when they need help the most. It is fascinating to work with brilliant doctors and surgeons and to help them use the wonderful equipment which helps to save lives. There's a happy team spirit in any hospital, and you will be working with like-minded girls who have an absorbing interest in common with you.

How do you become a nurse, then? Here are the facts you need to know.

How to qualify

For training as State Registered Nurse you will need G.C.E. at 'O' level in two subjects, one of which must be English Language (or Welsh), together with a letter from the Head of your school showing that you have reached a satisfactory standard in at least five subjects.

If you haven't reached this level you will be required to take an entrance test, set by the General Council of Nursing.

There are certain exceptions to this broad rule, and on this and other matters relating to nursing as a career you can get full details from the Nursing Recruitment Service, King Edward's Hospital Fund, 6 Cavendish Square, London, W.1.

If you feel that you cannot attain the educational standard needed to be a State Registered Nurse, there is a wide and interesting range of nursing duties that you can perform as a *State Enrolled Nurse*. Here you do not need the G.C.E. qualification.

Once accepted, you will be expected to take a three-year training course for State Registration, or a simpler two-year course for State Enrolment.

At what age?

Training for both types of nursing starts at 18. There are a number of useful things you can do to fill the gap if you leave school before that: work in a nursery school, a pre-nursing course which may be available at your school, suitable evening classes and Red Cross work, and anything which brings you into contact with people.

The conditions and pay

Conditions in hospitals nowadays are very good. If you live 'in', as you probably will, you are likely to have your own nicely furnished bedroom, and there will be recreation and study rooms too. There is a lively social life in nurses' homes. The pay during training is adequate and will leave you reasonable pocket money too.

Once trained, a State Registered Nurse starts earning at a rate of about £10 per week (higher in London and also higher in Psychiatric Hospitals). A State Enrolled Nurse starts at about £9 per week.

Prospects

Once trained there are many ways for you to specialise. You can take up midwifery, district nursing or health visiting, specialise in the care of children or the mentally sick, and you can go on to be a nurse tutor, assistant matron or matron.

Here is a career indeed, with plenty of choice to do what interests you most and plenty of scope to attain high qualifications and a really responsible job.

SOCCER SUCCESS

by

MATT BUSBY One of the most successful Managers, world football

SO you want to be a footballer? You're not a bad judge, either! Football, as a profession, has a great deal to offer every youngster. A couple of years ago, when strict control on earnings was enforced in the Football League, soccer was hardly an attractive career. Today, things are very different—with tremendous rewards awaiting boys with talent.

I must stress, however, that the game provides a good living *only* for those with outstanding ability. In other words, boys, and their parents, of course, must be quite certain that the potential talent is there before turning professional.

Success brings an excellent income, plus the glamour of film star headlines. Failure, on the other hand, can lead to heartache. That is why I always advise soccer-mad youngsters to take up an apprenticeship in another trade—just in case things should go wrong. My own son Sandy wanted to play football all day and every day, but before taking it up on a full-time basis, he served his time as an engineer. I am sure he never regretted having two strings to his bow.

Having ensured—as far as possible—that you have sufficient skill, and that you are not entirely dependent on soccer for your living, your next step must be to safeguard your physical condition. This does not mean a Spartan existence to the exclusion of all other pleasures. It does mean dedication to the game, in every way.

As Stanley Matthews approaches his fiftieth year, and STILL manages to do a first class job of work for his club Stoke City every Saturday, this outstanding player is obviously proving his keep-fit methods are correct. How does Matthews keep it up at an age when most other players are well past retirement?

Matthews does not drink alcoholic beverages, he never smokes. What is more, he goes to bed at the right time, eats the right sort of food, and never shirks any training chores. I am convinced that many other great footballers could have lasted as long as Stanley had they been similarly dedicated to physical fitness.

My advice, then, to any boys wishing to become footballers is simple:–
(1) Work to improve your natural skill.
(2) Treat your body as you would a delicate precision instrument by living sensibly.

Football has become a world-wide game:

The Big Catch!

Take the initial letter of each object and re-arrange them to spell the name of the fish that Billy Beaver caught

HELP BILLY TO FIND HIS LOG

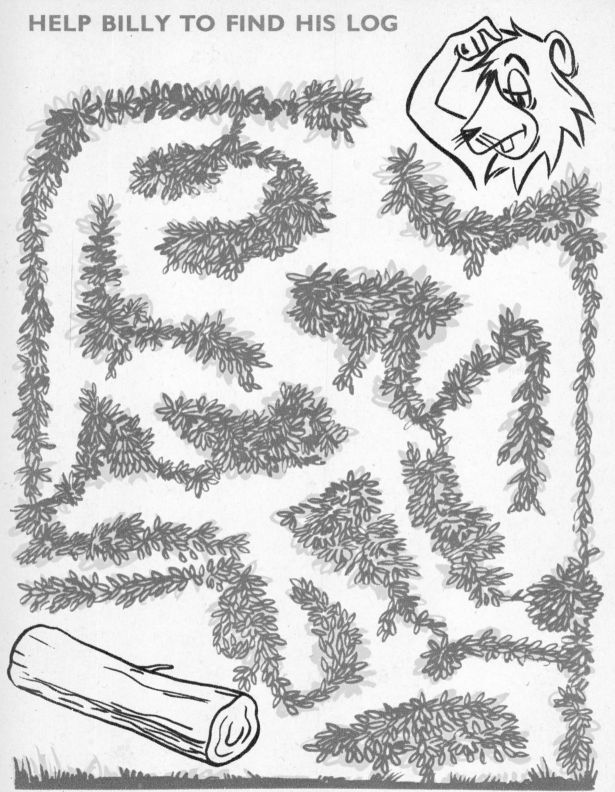

Billy Beaver can't remember where he left his log. Can you find a clear way through the leaves for him?

WHO GOES THERE?

JOIN THE BUBBLES NUMBERED 1 TO 19 TO DISCOVER WHAT MADE THIS SCHOOL OF FISH BREAK UP AND SWIM AWAY.

JOURNALIST

Nancy Spain

there would have been no story told about her. It was because she went to the ball, with her rags turned to a smashing dress, and because she messed it all up on the stroke of midnight that the story was worth telling.

Think of the stories that you swap with your pals, and you will be fascinated by the way they listen where there are big contrasts in the tale.

Now. How to begin as a reporter.

Get inside a newspaper office or a TV studio. It doesn't matter how, or at how small a wage to begin with. A bright boy or girl, who is just running messages, has a wonderful chance, on the spot as long as his eyes, ears and brain are open.

Also it doesn't matter where the TV studio or newspaper office may be. It is the ambition of every would-be top reporter to work in Fleet Street or at the TV offices in London. But some of the liveliest stories, and best journalism in the world is still put out in the provinces. Reporting on a Mayor's tea party or a Bazaar may seem a bit dull to you, but it needn't be. You can always find some element of contrast and bring it out in the telling of the story.

A cub reporter starts at £21 10s. a week in London's Fleet Street, less in the provinces. A top writer can earn as much as £100 a week.

But don't forget, if you want to succeed, the journalist's life is tough. It is full of hard work, late hours, and black looks.

Against that there is travel, opportunity to meet thousands of people, amongst them the great stars of stage, screen and TV . . . and an endless day by day variety.

The journalist's life is never dull!

T HE life of a journalist is the free-est in the world. I can't remember a time when I *didn't* want to live it, and when I was seven years' old I earned my first money (10/6d) writing a competition essay in a children's magazine.

In fact, it isn't necessary to be a *writer* to be a journalist. Good writing can even be a hindrance in telling a news story, for writers often want to linger over a story, telling it in flowery language and so wasting the reader's time. A good journalist goes for *facts*. He often has no time to write them up, and telephones his 'stuff' through to the office where a 're-write' man will cloak it in words for him.

Of course both boys and girls can be journalists, but I find it easier (in writing about it) to refer to the budding journalist as 'he'.

So train your eyes to observe, your ears to hear and over hear, and your brain to record it all, and recognise a 'good story'.

It is a little hard to explain to a non journalist what a good story is. There is always a great contrast in the tale, between poverty and riches, danger and peace, success and failure—or various combinations of all these things.

If Cinderella had stayed in her kitchen

TUBBY takes the CAKE

GEORGE ANSTRUTHER FITZ-GERALD SEYMOUR CARMODY rose from the pinewood table in the big kitchen of the Silver Horseshoe Ranch with a fat sigh of repletion and a lot of stertorous breathing.

His movements were laboured and sluggish, for he had just feasted not wisely but too well. In fact, the only quick thing about him was his darting gaze as it suddenly came to him that he didn't wish to be caught with the shattered remains of Aunt Hester's deep apple pie!

He knew that pie had been baked for supper for five—but it had smiled up at him so invitingly that he just couldn't resist carving himself a slice. And, alas, one slice had led to another, then another and another and another.

It was his total failure to resist the lure of any food within reaching distance which had earned him the nickname of Tubby.

Back home in England he was known far and wide as the Porker of Porterhouse School and it was generally agreed throughout the Remove that nothing eatable was safe from Tubby Carmody unless it was nailed down and surrounded by electrified wire.

"Greedy hog," "fat pig" and "George the Gorger" were epithets freely bestowed on Tubby's head.

He had expected to be spending his summer holidays with some cousins in Hampshire, but at the end of term an invitation came for him to go out to Arizona and stay with his Uncle Will Lawless, Aunt Hester and his cousins Tom and Eddie.

The news was received with a sigh of relief by Tubby's cousins in Hampshire—a relief tinged with sympathy for the other cousins in far-off America who were about to have their first experience of Tubby's majestic eating habits.

But with his father's stern warnings ringing in his fat ears, Tubby had manfully restrained himself during the first week of his stay. By iron self-discipline, he kept himself well in hand and never ate more than enough for three fully-grown men at any meal.

The healthy outdoor life and exhilarating air of Arizona were enough to give anyone a keen appetite and the Lawless family were all good trenchermen—but even when restraining himself Tubby was first at the table and last to get up.

So far, though, he hadn't disgraced himself by raiding the larder. But now the deed was done and Tubby quaked at the thought of what Aunt Hester was likely to say if she discovered that he was the culprit.

His uncle and cousins had ridden out to the range and Tubby was supposed to join them. With what had looked like the biggest apple pie in Arizona reposing inside him, Tubby didn't feel much like riding, but prudence suggested that he'd better saddle-up quick—before Aunt Hester returned from a neighbouring visit.

Tubby was starting for the door when he heard the sound.

"Crumbs!" he moaned. "Aunt Hester's back early . . ." He glanced wildly round, then moved his fat body across the kitchen at a surprising turn of speed and wedged himself in the pantry.

The sound, which had seemed like distant footsteps, grew louder. Now it was the heavy tread of booted feet.

"Must be one of the cowpunchers," Tubby told himself, though it was odd because he knew the ranch hands were all out working.

Scarcely daring to breathe, Tubby risked a peep through the slit of the almost-closed door.

His eyes nearly popped out of his head, for two powerful men had entered the ranch, their hands resting on strapped-down gun holsters.

And each man wore a vivid red bandana across the lower half of his face!

"Oo . . . er," croaked Tubby—but not aloud.

One of the intruders was speaking.

"They's all out on the range, Jud—I guess we got the place to ourselves."

"Yeah, but th' thing is where does he keep it, Butch?"

Butch shrugged. "It'll not be in the kitchen, that's for sure," he said. "C'mon—let's go."

"Where?"

"Rancher Lawless'll have a study or office or sump'n, I reckon that's where it'll be," Butch answered. His piggy eyes glared at his companion. "You wanna use yore head, stupid—where else could it be, for Pete's sake?" he demanded.

"Sure." Jud's gaze went to the kitchen table. "Seems like some *hombre's* been eating powerful well," he said. "How about us fillin' up from the pantry . . ."

He moved towards it and Tubby shook so violently he felt sure the whole ranch would tremble with him.

Jud's hand was actually on the door knob when Butch snarled: "Whaddya figger this is—a picnic? We gotta get the stuff and beat it outa here afore they ride back. Get going . . ."

The heavy feet clumped across the

16

kitchen and down the hall. Tubby let out some breath and tiptoed after them. He held the kitchen's interior door open just wide enough to see the two masked men vanish into Uncle Will's den.

There was a rending sound, then a jubilant exclamation.

"Got it . . . gee, there's ten thousand dollars in the cash-box!"

"Haw, haw! Rancher Lawless sure is goin' to look like a sick steer when he finds he ain't got his payroll tomorrow!"

"Hee, hee! I'd sure like to see his face."

"I reckon we'll kind of have to deny ourselves that pleasure on account of we'll be safe in Mesa City spending his dough," cackled Butch.

"You betcha!"

"They's goin' to be a real hot time in the old town tonight. Let's go!"

The bandits came out of the den and Tubby jumped back into the pantry. He had only just got the door closed when the two stalked through the kitchen and out on to the patio.

Tubby glanced round urgently. He *must* do something! If only he had a shotgun! There was one, but it wasn't in the kitchen and by the time he could get to the weapon the rascally Butch and Jud would be riding like the wind.

But Tubby, though he had often done much to earn the name of "greedy hog," was no coward. If he couldn't hold the robbers up with a shotgun then the least he could do was to follow them.

His own horse was in the livery stable and he could get there unseen through a side door.

When he swung himself into the saddle Butch and Jud were already some distance away, heading due south down the old stagecoach trail on the thirty-mile ride to Mesa City.

Tubby gritted his teeth and sent his mount into a steady gallop after them.

He hadn't a very clear idea of just what he was going to do if and when he came close to the bandits . . . but somehow, he told himself, he was going to do something!

Butch Billings reined-in under the overhang of a high bluff.

"We've put plenty of miles between us and the Lawless spread—maybe twelve-fifteen, I guess," he said. "I reckon that's far enough for us to rest up a little over yonder . . ." The bandit aimed a stained forefinger at a clearing just off the trail.

The two cantered into the clearing, dismounted and tethered their horses at the side of a bubbling brook of clear mountain water.

Both men sprawled on the bank to drink from the little stream, then sat under a tree rolling cigarettes with practised fingers.

"Say a quarter hour to rest up and we'll be on the last lap into Mesa City," Butch mused. "Even if Lawless has gotten back to the ranch and even if he's missed the payroll we can still outdistance him by a long ways . . . and once in Mesa City we're safe."

"Yeah—if any of the Lawless bunch show their faces in Mesa we'll know how to take care of 'em," chuckled Jud. "That sure is one wide-open town . . ."

"And we got friends there."

"Including the sheriff . . . haw, haw, haw!"

"If Rancher Lawless moseys into Mesa he'll sure enough be wearing lead buttons on his vest afore long," grinned Butch.

He blew a stream of blue smoke into the still, warm air.

"Kinda peaceful here," he said. "Nary a *hombre* within many miles, I'd say."

But Butch was wrong.

Though riding far behind, Tubby had seen the distant figures turn off the trail and make for the clearing.

Tubby rode on a short way, then dismounted himself and led his horse into the thickly wooded foothills.

He hitched the reins to a tree branch and picked his way slowly and with great care through the scrub and brushwood, testing his not inconsiderable weight on every twig before going on, for now even a small snapping sound could betray his nearness.

As he walked with ever - increasing deliberation the trees became thicker and taller until, though sundown was some time ahead, it seemed almost dark—a sort of still, eerie twilight.

Away in the distance a coyote howled mournfully, then stopped, and no sound came to Tubby in the vast stillness of the forest.

Slowly and even more carefully now, he made his way. Then, just when he was starting to wonder if his sense of direction had played him tricks, he almost walked straight out into the clearing!

But with a sudden, sharp intake of breath, he darted behind a massive cottonwood, from which vantage point he could see without being seen by the payroll bandits.

Butch was gleefully thumbing a huge wad of dollar bills, watched by Jud's greedy eyes.

"Yessir—we're sure gonna have one swell time with all this dough," Butch gloated. He glanced suddenly at his crony, one hand making a snaking movement towards his gun.

"Don't get no ideas about taking it off me, Jud," Butch said in a nasty voice.

Jud's eyes widened innocently.

"As if I would! We're buddies, ain't we?"

"Sure . . . but, jest th' same don't get no ideas . . . *whassat*?"

Butch sat bolt upright, then scrambled to his feet.

"I didn't hear nothing, Butch . . ."

"I fancied I saw a shadow or sump'n," Butch muttered. He bent his head, listening intently. Then he shrugged. "Guess I must've imagined it," he said.

Behind the big cottonwood Tubby breathed relief. He *had* moved, to get a slightly better view, and his bulk must have loomed darker against the greenery.

But now that he was here he still didn't know what he could do. If he trailed the robbers into Mesa City that wouldn't help —he'd have even less chance there of getting Uncle Will's payroll money back.

Jud went down to the stream for the horses and Butch stood watching him, the wad of dollars still in one greasy hand.

The other hand moved slowly and methodically downwards to the handle of his huge Frontier Colt six-shooter.

An evil grin spread over Butch's villainous features. He brought the gun out and up—aiming it straight at Jud's back!

There was a split second in which time seemed to stand still for Tubby. Then he let out a long, high, piercing yell.

Whoo . . . oooo . . . eeeee . . . Whooo . . . eeeeeee . . . eeeeeeeee . . .

It was a sound like nothing Butch Billings had ever heard in his life.

He leaped inches off the ground in fright, and at the same moment Jud wheeled . . . and saw the gun in his so-called partner's hand.

"Yuh . . . yuh . . . yuh was a-going to . . ."

Whooooo . . . eeeeeee . . . ayee . . . ayeeeeee . . .

"I wasn't tryin' to gun yuh, Jud," screamed Butch. "They's some wild monster in the trees . . . yuh can hear it . . . OW!"

He made the last exclamation as Jud flung himself at him.

"There's sump'n there all right," panted Jud, "but I'll deal with that when I've dealt with you and . . ." The rest of his words were lost as the two men thudded violently to the ground and rolled over and over locked in desperate combat.

Thud!

Bang!

Wham!

KER-PLUNK!!

As the bandits grappled with each other the wad of money flew from Butch's grasp . . . and landed almost at Tubby's feet.

It was no more than the work of a second for Tubby to grab the roll off the ground and leap backwards into the trees.

But it was just time enough for Butch to see him.

"Some *hombre's* taken the payroll!" he yelled.

"Don't give me that, you double-crossing rattlesnake!" bellowed Jud.

With a mighty effort, Butch managed to roll free. He came up fast on his feet with his gun held far out.

"I tell yuh I seen him, Jud," he roared. "Look . . . the wad's vanished!"

Jud's eyes almost started from their sockets.

"It was a boy, a kid about fifteen—a fat kid," Butch grated. "We gotta get after him!"

Jud rushed towards the trees, but Butch thrust out a hand and hauled him back.

"Use yore head, stupid," he sneered. "If we get the horses we can ride back up the trail and catch him as he comes out—he can't have walked. He'll have left his mount somewheres . . ."

"You're right," Jud said. "Wait till I get my hands on that thieving varmint!"

On and on pelted Tubby. Never—not even on the celebrated occasion when he had been chased across the playing fields by Herbert Croker after raiding the latter's tuck hamper—had Tubby made such fast speed.

At all costs he had to get to his horse before the villainous pair could close in on him.

His breath came in mighty gulps and his chest felt as if iron bands were being wrapped round it, but fear lent him wings.

Tubby practically skimmed the ground in his headlong flight! He grabbed the reins and swung himself back in the saddle and was off up the trail in a series of lightning movements.

Craaa . . . aacck!

Wheeee . . . eeeeeeee!

PING!!

A bullet whammed into the side of

a sandstone bluff, and ricochetted off.

"Crumbs—they're shooting at me . . . ooooer!" yelped Tubby. He urged his horse into renewed speed.

Far behind him he could hear the muffled thud-thud-thud of pounding hoofs, but even in his panic he realised that the two robbers weren't narrowing the distance.

Tubby, though fat, still weighed less than either Butch or Jud and his horse was thus able to widen the gap between him and his pursuers.

A few miles more and the fine spreading buildings of the Silver Horseshoe Ranch came into view.

Tubby rode the remaining distance like a whirlwind, flung himself off and rushed into the ranch-house clutching the precious payroll. He rammed the money into his pants pockets as he went through into the kitchen . . . almost straight into the arms of Aunt Hester.

"Tubby! What do you mean by it?" Aunt Hester's voice rose questioningly.

"Help . . . I mean . . . look here, they're after . . . I mean any minute now . . ."

"Tubby—what *are* you babbling about?" It was Tom Lawless, who had come into the kitchen. Eddie, grinning widely, was close behind him.

Tubby was still struggling for words when Rancher Lawless joined them.

"Somebody," said Aunt Hester thoughtfully, "somebody has just about eaten the apple pie." She eyed Tubby for a long moment.

Tubby was now practically dancing a jig with excitement and apprehension.

"The . . . the bandits . . . I mean the robbers . . ."

"The *whatters*?" grinned Eddie.

"The bandits," moaned Tubby, "they've been here."

"What—pinching Mom's pie?" said Tom with a chuckle.

"I tell you . . ."

"It wouldn't be a very fat bandit, by any chance?" said Eddie.

"Won't somebody *please* listen to me?"

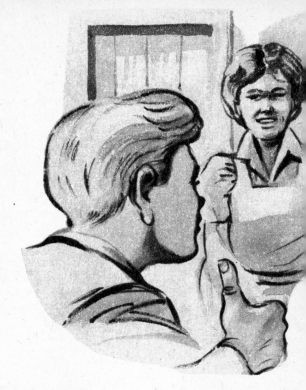

wailed Tubby. He turned desperately to Rancher Lawless. "It's your money . . . they stole it . . . the money you drew to pay the hands, Uncle Will . . ."

Rancher Lawless put a hand on his shoulder.

"Now what . . ." he began.

"Two men wearing bandanas came here while you were out," gasped Tubby, beginning to get coherent words out at last. "I saw them after I . . . er . . . well, that is, I saw them. They called each other Butch and Jud and . . ."

Something flickered in Will Lawless's keen grey eyes. "Butch Billings and Jud Janson!" he exclaimed. "I saw those two coyotes skulking around the bank in town this morning. By Harry, if they've . . ."

Tubby grinned. "You don't need to look, Uncle Will," he said smoothly. "I recovered the money from them . . . that's why I wasn't here when you all returned."

He held out two fistfuls of notes.

Four pairs of eyes goggled at the dollar bills, then at Tubby.

"But them galoots are dangerous," said Will Lawless seriously.

"How come you got the money from them, Tubby?"

"I . . . I can't stop to tell you now, Uncle Will," said Tubby urgently. "They're hot on my trail . . . they're liable to be here any minute and . . ."

Will Lawless's mouth hardened.

"You mean them varmints are coming *here*?" he demanded incredulously. "You must be crazy, Tubby . . ."

From the door a voice rasped.

"Naw . . . the kid ain't crazy, Lawless . . ." Butch Billings stepped into the kitchen. Jud fanned out from him. Both desperadoes had their guns aimed.

"Reach for it, you guys," snapped Butch. "And don't nobody try anything unless you-all want to wind up on Boot Hill!"

Aunt Hester shrank back with a small sound. Tom and Eddie glared balefully at the bandits. Their father turned slowly, eyeing the intruders contemptuously.

"You won't get away with it, either of you," he said harshly.

Butch sneered. "We came here masked and owing to that darned fat kid we've had

to come back and now you knows us," he said. "But it ain't gonna do you no good. We're gonna rope you bunch together and stuff some gags in yore mouths . . . and by the time yore riders free you we'll be long gone."

Jud, who was still circling the room, stopped and snarled: "Hand over that there payroll, Lawless, or I plugs yuh!"

Rancher Lawless held his ground.

A leering smile split Jud's evil face.

"Okay, suit yoreself," he grated. "Either you hands over the payroll or I wing one of these hyar lads of yorn . . ."

Will Lawless bit hard down on his lip. Then, without a sound, he handed the heavy wad of notes over.

As Jud took them Butch put out a gnarled hand and grabbed them from him. "We'll divvy up later," he said.

Eddie Lawless laughed. "So you don't even trust each other," he said.

Butch slapped him a stinging blow across the mouth and Eddie reeled back.

"Okay, we'll divvy the split right here and now, Jud," Butch said. He stared round the room. "Where's that fat kid gotten himself to?" he asked.

It was a point which had occurred to Lawless. He had seen Tubby backing away when the bandits came in, but in the excitement since then he hadn't noticed any more.

"Waal, it makes no diff'rence now," gloated Butch. "We got the money and as soon as we got you birds roped together kind of nice and tight me an' Jud'll divide the loot and beat it and . . . Ow . . . Ouch . . . OW!"

"Eeeeee . . . OUCH!" shrieked Jud.

Then they were both staggering backwards, their rascally faces almost unseen behind a vast sticky mass of melting chocolate, cream fillings and slabs of cake.

Tubby, who had backed into the pantry, had leaped out with a magnificent and still-warm chocolate cake in each hand. His hands had spread backwards and then hurled both the cakes with unerring marksmanship!

Whoosh . . . OW . . . Wassit . . . OUCH!

Butch and Jud were reeling about with their hands clawing at their faces to get the oozing mass from their eyes.

By the time they could see again both were looking down the barrels of Rancher Lawless's shining six-guns!

Above the commotion Aunt Hester's voice said: "Oh dear . . . and I'd only just baked those cakes for Sunday!"

Tom and Eddie were clapping Tubby on the shoulders, laughing helplessly at the hapless bandits' suddenly crushed appearance.

"Good old Tubby!" shouted Tom.

"Three cheers for Tubby!" cried Eddie.

Aunt Hester put an arm round him and said: "Never mind the cakes, Tubby, you've saved us!"

In a few moments Butch and Jed were securely trussed up and awaiting the arrival of the sheriff's posse.

"Robbing a payroll will put these two behind bars for a long time to come," said Rancher Lawless sternly.

Aunt Hester eyed the bandits grimly.

"Why, it must have been these men who ate all my lovely apple pie," she said. "They ought to get a special sentence just for that."

In the midst of all the praise for his conduct Tubby shifted his feet uneasily.

"I . . . er . . . I'm afraid it was me, Aunt Hester," he said. "I saw that pie and . . . and . . . well, I just couldn't resist it . . ." He grinned and added: "It was the most scrumptious pie anybody ever baked and you ought to be given a medal for it, Aunt Hester!"

Aunt Hester smiled happily.

"Do you know, Tubby, that's the nicest compliment I've ever been paid," she said. "Your uncle and your cousins eat all my pies and never say a word and . . ."

"Now, now, Mother," began Rancher Lawless, laughing.

"You mean Tubby scoffed that enormous pie entirely unaided?" said Eddie, staring.

"Of course," said Aunt Hester, "which proves it was a real fine pie or he could never have done it."

"I'm sorry, Aunt Hester," said Tubby contritely.

"Nonsense," cried Aunt Hester. "And for that lovely compliment you paid me I'm going to bake you a special personal pie all to yourself every day for the rest of your stay with us!"

And she did.

Which is why, when Tubby finally got back to Porterhouse School, he not only had many happy memories of his holiday in the Wild West but quite a few more inches round his middle!

FUN IN THE SANDHILLS

Here is a happy holiday scene for you to colour

SAILING AWAY

Paint or Crayon each part of the picture with the appropriate colour from the key below.
Y=Yellow.　O=Orange.　LB=Light Blue.　DB=Deep Blue.　LG=Light Green.　DG=Deep Green.
BR=Brown.　G=Grey.　P=Purple.　R=Red.

so you want to
be a CYCLIST

Eileen Sheridan

BOYS and girls, if you have set your heart on cycling, then just keep on pestering your parents to buy you a bike. There is no other activity which offers so much for so little expense.

If you live in a town, you can get out into the country and enjoy the fun of meandering along the little lanes, swooping silently down hills, or having a picnic by some lovely little river. And later on, a trip of 60 to 80 miles in a day should be well within your capacity. So, in the summer, many of you can get to the sea.

Of course, you will want to have the company of other young folk. Here again cycling can give you all you need. By joining a cycling club or the Youth Hostel's Association, happy companionship is yours for the asking. The Cyclists' Touring Club has branches all over the country.

It caters for every type and age group. It provides a most comprehensive programme of home and continental tours, together with all manner of competition rallies, and social activities.

So much for pleasure! Competitively too, the bike can provide plenty of outlet. There are four distinct types of racing events — "time trialling," "massed start" racing, "track sport," and "long distance record breaking."

Finally, for sheer economy, there is nothing to beat the bike. One can save on fares to school, to work, even shopping expeditions for mum. In fact a bike is worth its weight in gold. As an example of the combination of speed and economy possible, I must mention my own experience in the London to Paris air race which took place three years ago.

Accompanied by my 13-years-old son Clive, I rode from Marble Arch to Southend Airport, took a plane to Le Bourget Airport, and rode to the Arc de Triomphe. Our total journey took just under four hours. Only one hour longer than the time taken by Nancy Spain, who travelled in a Rolls Royce over the same route, using the same plane. And to keep within *her* time record the Rolls often touched 100 m.p.h.

With regard to the subjects of gearing and of position on your bicycle, I advise you to consult the many excellent text books on cycling available at your local public library. Remember, except when racing, cycling should never be hard work. You should at all times be relaxed and comfortable on your machine.

Here's a useful little tip, always take a bar of chocolate or a packet of raisins when going for a ride, as a standby against any sudden attack of what cyclists call "hunger knock." Remember your Highway Code, and always give clear and timely hand signals.

Those youngsters who pass the National Cycling Proficiency Test can become members of the Cyclists' Touring Club for only 5/6d. annually. And remember—the C.T.C. address is 3, Craven Hill, London W.2.

Happy cycling!

Eileen Sheridan.

The Adventures of Billy Beaver

by

NANCY SPAIN

illustrated by W.S. Greenhalgh

BILLY BEAVER WAS THE CHAMPION LOG ROLLER IN THE WHOLE OF CANADA...

AND SO...

...BILLY FACED THE MIGHTY ATLANTIC OCEAN...

...BILLY FELT SICK

THERE WERE STORMS IN THE ATLANTIC...

BILLY WISHED HE HADN'T COME ... BUT BILLY STRUGGLED ON AND ONE DAY HE SAW A LINER

BUT THE LINER SAILED AWAY IN THE DISTANCE. BILLY WAS SAD.

AND BILLY SEES IT IS NOT A MAN, BUT A GIRL, BEAUTIFUL BRIGITTE BUNNY, WHO IS DROWNING.

QUICK AS A FLASH HE HAULS HER TO HIS LOG.

BOATS ARE LOWERED AND BRIGITTE AND BILLY ARE SOON HAULED ABOARD

29

MY BEST HOLIDAY EVER

by Charlie Drake

SPEAKING as an ex-Butlin Redcoat, says Charlie Drake, all the time I spent in the camps (in spite of the fact that I was doing a job of work) were relaxing and wonderful. So they would be the best, except that they weren't supposed to be holidays.

So I'll have to go for the most memorable.

I spent an extraordinary time in Cumberland once, when I was voted King of Sport. Lord Lonsdale had me as house guest and I kept my end up at huntin', shootin' and the rest of it . . . And once the Editor of this here Annual took me and fellow comedian Eric Sykes up to Liverpool to play off a great golf match. N. Spain and C. Drake played M. Bygraves and E. Sykes and beat them with such gamesmanship that Eric Sykes hit the wrong ball and forfeited the match. It was a wonderful day that, at Lytham St. Annes, on the old links, with larks singing, etc. and the jokes and all that went on until we all climbed into the midnight train for London.

Yes, a change is the best holiday—no matter whether it's from job or school, to home or heaven by the sea.

Many of the other stage folk go abroad . . . Tommy Steele and Adam Faith are always going to Spain, for example . . . but to me there's never been anywhere like Skegness, Clacton, Bognor Regis, Pwllheli and of course all the other BUTLIN HOLIDAY CAMPS. Frankly, my darlings, I prefer to speak English.

Huckleberry Hound
THE GORILLA GRABBER

36

JUKE BOX JURY MYSTERY

BY Nancy Spain

PETER lived in Streatham by a big garage where all the lorries pulled up to fuel before they went swinging off on their journeys up and down the great roads of England. Peter was twelve and he had two passions in life: car number spotting (which he could do with the lorries) and that famous BBC programme Juke Box Jury.

Peter went to school during the week, and when he came home on weekday evenings there was homework (of course) and on Saturdays there was Juke Box Jury. In the autumn and winter Peter's Dad used to sit,

frowning at a little table, writing down the football results (which are always given directly before Juke Box Jury) just in case he had won anything on the pools (he never did!) and so the whole family were there together, most cosily, to watch and argue about Juke Box Jury. Peter often thought that was why he was so fond of this particular programme, because it was such a warm feeling, all the family together sitting watching and listening and Dad still muttering quietly about the teams that had let him down, and Mum muttering (less quietly) about the records she didn't like, and the panelists with whom she disagreed. So, really, there was never a week that Peter missed Juke Box Jury and he looked forward to the programme all the week, particularly on Friday.

It was 'particularly on Friday' because it was arithmetic last period on Friday, and Peter was bad at arithmetic. Often he had to stay after the last bell had gone, to do the work again. So Juke Box Jury was something to look forward to, and quite often in the margins of the arithmetic exercise book there would be little pictures of gramophone records and faces very like Kenny Ball and his Jazzmen and Cliff Richard and The Shadows. So while Peter was making wild guesses about 'Which Cistern out of A, B and C empties itself the fastest' his mind was really full of the sound of music.

"As if anyone cared about cisterns," thought Peter, pushing his desk back, and slamming his exercise book shut, and diving through the door. He shot the exercise book into Mr Maitland's shelf (it was Old Maitland who had given him Returned Work) and he started to run.

Soon he was out of the school gates and scudding along the High Street. It was a misty, drizzly autumn evening, more damp than frosty and Peter was soon out of breath and had to slow up. By the time he got to the garage he was really loitering, and also fumbling round in his satchel for his ball-point pen and his notebook in case there were any funny numbers to spot. Then he came to a dead stop, and he gave a little whistle. Because there (of all things) was a BBC lorry: a huge one, one of the kind that go all over the place, carrying cameras and scenery and goodness knows what besides. Peter had never seen a BBC lorry close to before and he wrote down the number AJA 423 before he moved in close. He wondered if there was any chance of getting acquainted with the driver, and so somehow get a ticket for Juke Box Jury. Peter had always longed to be one of the teen-agers

who hold up the records in the front row, and so make the deciding vote of Hit or Miss. (Being twelve was so nearly thirteen he knew he would qualify).

So Peter moved in closer to have a look at the van. There was a man crouching by the wheel. He had his back turned to Peter.

"Mister—" said Peter.

The man swung round with a sort of snarl. Peter jumped back, for he was afraid he was going to hit him.

"—sorry if I made you jump I—" Peter went on.

Even in the half-dark the man was frightening. He was quite young. Peter saw his face clearly in the street lights, which had come on. He had side-burns like Elvis, but he was fair. He had a sharp nose, like a ferret. He was holding the compressed air machine in his hand. He had been blowing up the tyres.

"Who d'you think you are creeping up on me like that?" he shouted, squirting compressed air at Peter. A blast hit Peter in the chest and he staggered back. It felt warmish but very hard and peculiar.

"Who d'you think you are hanging around?" he shouted.

Stumbling backwards Peter now fell over a watering can that was used for filling radiators. And one of his school books slid from under his arm and went slithering across the pavement. The man kicked it. And then Peter was really frightened. Because suddenly there was a wicked looking automatic pistol in his hand. He had snatched it from under his arm, so he must have been wearing one of those shoulder holsters like the gangsters in the pictures. Peter was now really scared. He stooped and picked up his school book and then he was off like a shot, running through the drizzle to his own flat. The school book was soaked, wet with mud and ruined, and Peter was panting by the time he had raced up the stairs to his own front door. It couldn't have been a real BBC van then. Surely the drivers of those were more old and solid, and certainly they wouldn't have pistols.

Mum was annoyed when he got in.

"Why're you late? Oh my. What a mess. Your pants are all mud. Why're you so white? White's sheet. Wait till it dries then I'll brush it off." She didn't let him get a word in edgeways; otherwise he'd have told her then and there about the man with the gun. Instead, he settled to his tea. But he could scarcely eat it. Should he tell Mum? No, she'd only say he'd made it up. He munched away as best he could. But that face and the gun kept returning to him. And each time it did, it put him off his tea. Peter now choked tea and chased a few stray beans round his plate. What was the number of the van? AJA 423. When is a door not a door, when it's AJAr. Ha, ha, ha . . .

Peter shoved his plate into the sink, rinsed it quickly and sneaked along to his own room. There was an old Victorian washstand in there, that Mum had brought from her own home in the country, she said. It had a marble top and was very solid and Peter often drew there. It was easier than drawing in the margins of a muddy arithmetic book. He had plenty of paper in his old drawing book. He tried to draw the man from memory. A sharp nose—So. Eyebrows up in a tilt. A cleft in the chin. Thin mouth. What clothes had he been wearing?

Winkle picker shoes. Jeans. Black leather jacket. More like one of the 'Ton' motorbike brigade than a BBC man.

"Don't forget to brush your teeth," shouted Mum along the passage and Peter grumbled that he was just going to. So he shut the drawing book and went along to the bathroom and forgot the whole thing. For a while, that is. Until next evening, just before the football results when Dad showed Peter two faces in the evening paper. Drawings. Put together from a Police Identikit they were, these faces. Dad and Peter were sitting together in front of the television, and Peter also had his drawing book and was just messing about. Dad who was rather proud of Peter's talent as an artist was watching him. Dad pointed the stem of his pipe at the two faces.

"I don't see how anybody can ever recognise anybody from these things," said Dad, disgustedly. "The two faces are supposed to represent the same fellow, but they look totally different to me . . . Look . . ." He held the paper out to Peter who looked at the faces silently. Mum wasn't there, she was bustling round in the kitchen.

"I don't know," said Peter slowly. "They do have certain whatsername, characteristics in common. Like a sharp nose and a thin mouth and a cleft chin." Somewhere inside him a penny seemed to drop. "Well." he said. "Well. I wonder—"

"Wonder what?" said Dad. But Dad was absent-minded now because the football results were just coming, and the racing (which didn't interest Dad) was slowly coming to an end.

"This man," began Peter, "Look." And he began to scrabble through his drawing book to find the sketch he had made of the driver of the 'BBC van'. . .

"Wait a minute, lad," said Dad, now breathing heavily and concentrating like mad as he checked his duplicate football coupon. "Just wait until I've done this football . . ."

Peter said nothing. He simply sat with his drawing book and the two pictures from the evening paper, staring backwards and forwards until his eyes were crossed in his head. Could it be? Could it possibly be? Or was he just imagining the whole thing and going to get laughed at for his pains.

The football results were slowly wound to a close. Through the 3rd division. Through the 4th division. Finally Dad stopped tut tut tutting and pulling at his lip.

"Dad," said Peter, as the final result flashed off the screen. "Do you think this man could be — ?"

Just then the music of Hit or Miss that is the signature tune of Juke Box Jury started to announce the Juke Box Jury session for that evening. Mum came back into the room, and Peter's chance was gone again. This time it wasn't Dad's fault, it was Peter's. He so enjoyed watching Juke Box Jury.

It was a very good panel, too. Alan Freeman, the disc jockey. And Pete Murray. Carole Carr and a visiting American star whose name I have forgotten. A woman. And one or two of the records were square enough to please Dad. After a close-up of Alan Freeman, jigging up and down in time to a very bouncy record indeed, the camera left the panel and began to pan slowly round the studio audience, picking up here a jigging foot, there a gormless looking female face with a shock of long hair and the mouth hanging open . . . And then suddenly a sharp ferrety face with a thin mouth and *side-burns like Elvis and a cleft chin* . . .

"NO!" shouted Peter, leaping up.

"Oh my, you did make me jump, whatever's the matter with the lad?" said Mum.

"Calm down Pete," said Dad.

Peter didn't care what they thought of him. He jumped and shouted and pointed.

"It's him, it's him, it's him, Dad!" he shouted. "The IDENTIKIT man. Look. In the evening paper. I saw him before at the garage. He threatened me. I was too scared to tell you. But look. *I* drew a picture of him. Look . . ."

Dad's annoyance gradually vanished. Mum calmed down. Everyone's hearts were beating, thumping, in their ears, throats. Dad made Peter go through the story from the beginning, slowly, bit by bit. It seemed woefully slow to Peter.

"Ring the BBC," shouted Mum, suddenly.

Mum was very inclined to get hysterical, which was another reason why Peter was quite glad he hadn't confided in her.

"Pointless," said Dad, which was a bit rude of him.

"A. It may be a recording from last week. I believe they record these things and put them on film. B. The BBC would be powerless without the police. No, no. It's Scotland Yard I'm ringing . . ."

The programme was still going on. It must have been the first time in his life that Peter watched and thought about something else. He found he was trembling as he looked at the set, in case the camera went to the audience again and showed the man's face. He could hardly hear Dad, who was being his slow emphatic down to earth self on the telephone.

"Yes," said Dad. "The Indentikit man. My son thinks he's seen him. Twice. Once outside a garage in Streatham, and once just this minute in the Juke Box Jury programme audience that's on now if you follow me. Yes. I can't tell if it's a live programme or not, but I thought if maybe it was—Oh yes. Right. 5 Acorn Buildings, Streatham. Yes. The lad and I will be waiting for you at the entrance. Thanks. The prowl car? Oh my. Thanks. Thanks very much."

And Dad rang off.

"What were you thankin' 'em for?" said Mum. "They should thank you more like—"

"Get your jacket, lad," said Dad, heavily. "We're going to the BBC." And he added, as though he could scarcely believe it himself. "In a prowl car. Police car. My word. Bring that drawing book. *And* the evening paper."

Peter afterwards thought he had scarcely counted up to 20 before they were sitting in the fast-moving prowl car, whizzing along the South Circular Road over Clapham Common towards Shepherd's Bush. As they went along Peter went through his story again and the men grunted. There were three policemen in the car, two in uniform and Sergeant Tomlinson, who was the leader. So Peter and Dad were rather squashed together in the back.

"Let's hope you're right, young feller-me-lad," said Sergeant Tomlinson, but not unkindly. "This seems to me a very slender series of coincidences. Still, there *are* coincidences in real life, just as there are in stories."

The prowl car drew up, with a jerk, outside the Television Theatre, which is on the 'green' at Shepherd's Bush. In those days Juke Box Jury was held there, instead of at TV Centre in Wood Lane. Just as the car drew up a commissionaire was bending down to open the doors, drawing back the bolts to allow the crowd to stream out into the clammy, head-lighty atmosphere of an autumn Saturday night.

Sergeant Tomlinson, looking big and bulky in his overcoat, shot across the pavement to the commissionaire at most uncommon speed.

"Hold the audience," he said. "Keep those doors locked. Yes, I am a police officer. Here is my identification."

Peter, Dad and Sergeant Tomlinson went on into the theatre. The last notes of John Barry's signature tune were just dying away, and people were beginning to move to the footlights for the autographs of the panel when Tomlinson's harsh voice of authority rang through the theatre.

"Everyone please sit down at once, and treat this as an extra part of the programme. I am a police officer from Scotland Yard."

There was an immediate buzz of excitement and startled faces turned towards them as Dad and Peter and Sergeant Tomlinson walked down the centre aisle. Peter, who had been looking everywhere for his man ever since they walked into the theatre, saw a familiar back view—leather jacket, jeans, battered winkle picker shoes—making for the pass door over on the right of the stage.

"There he is, Sergeant, sir," whispered Peter urgently. "There he is, over to the right, going by that camera."

For Peter was not so blinded by the excitement of being in a thrilling chase that he didn't notice pretty well everything to do with his beloved show.

Sergeant Tomlinson seemed to pounce down the seats. He ran to corner the man by the stage box. His huge pink hand descended on the man's shoulder in the shadows.

"Would you mind coming with me to the station?" said Tomlinson. "I have a few questions I want to ask—"

The man spun round. His right hand groped for his left armpit, where the pistol butt was plainly visible in the shoulder holster.

"Oh no you don't,' said Sergeant Tomlinson. "I've been warned about you and your pistol-packing proclivities."

The man side-stepped, tugging hopelessly at the pistol.

Sergeant Tomlinson twisted his arms behind his back and grabbed him just above the elbows.

"Here Baines. Here Reid. Help me."

There was a quick and dusty scuffle on the floor by the stage box as the two uniformed policemen joined in. Then Sergeant Tomlinson stood up with a pistol in his hand and the man (who Peter afterwards discovered was called Scobie Franton) was handcuffed.

"Impeding a police officer in the execution of his duty for a start," panted Sergeant Tomlinson, wiping dust from his knees. "Now then, young Peter, why are you so sure that this is the man who threatened you?"

Peter was about to open his mouth when Scobie Franton broke in. It was the first word he had spoken.

"You the nipper spotted me at Streatham.

Cor' . . . I eat boys like you for breakfast," he said, snarling.

All this and much, much more came out at the magistrates court, and later before a judge and jury before Peter pieced the whole story together properly.

But, briefly, this was what happened. Scobie (who was a very nasty piece of work indeed) was one of the key men in a gang of smash and grab raiders who specialised in jewel robberies, using a BBC van (or rather a van painted to look like a BBC van) as a cover vehicle. Scobie was the driver, and he had got the idea of using such a disguised vehicle because he actually lived in Shepherd's Bush, in Lime Grove, where another BBC vehicle never attracted attention.

On the Saturday night, however, when Peter had spotted him in the audience of Juke Box Jury, he had parked the van too near the stage door of the BBC Television Theatre and two innocent constables on the beat had complained that he was causing an obstruction. "Hey," they told him, "you can't leave that there 'ere."

Scobie had replied, "I'll go for further instructions then," and had dived into the stage door. Both BBC commissionaires had their backs turned and he had walked, gingerly and very quickly through on to the stage. Here he had panicked, tried to slip through into the auditorium and out into the street via the front doors, but the audience had just been filing in for Juke Box Jury. So he had sat down among them hoping to pass as one of the crowd. "And so he probably would have done if sharp-eyed Pete hadn't spotted him," Sergeant Tomlinson afterwards explained. So Scobie went to jail, for armed robbery. And because of the quick wits of a Juke Box Jury fan a dangerous criminal is now behind bars.

Peter is much older now, indeed he is a proper teen-ager: thirteen years old and still growing hard. But Juke Box Jury is still his favourite programme, and some people say that is where the mystery comes in . . .

The SPACE RACE

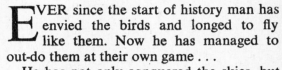

EVER since the start of history man has envied the birds and longed to fly like them. Now he has managed to out-do them at their own game . . .

He has not only conquered the skies, but he has begun to climb into and explore the great depths of the universe beyond the earth's atmosphere . . .

The force which holds man down on to the globe of the earth is known as *The Force of Gravity*. The further man gets away from the centre of the earth the less power the earth's 'pull' has over him.

The early flying machines could not leave the earth at great speed, and were therefore only capable of rising a few feet. Even an up-to-date jet plane only travels 30,000 feet up . . . about 10 miles, or the height of Everest . . . where the atmosphere becomes so thin we have to use 'pressurised cabins' and, sometimes, oxygen apparatus.

To escape the earth's pull, to go high enough into space ENORMOUS power had to be developed — so great it is difficult for us to imagine. And when he is in space man must reverse this power, 'kick' himself back into the 'gravity pull', and so return to earth.

You must not take these stages in the development of the Space Ships for granted. John Glenn, the American astronaut was born in 1921, and his mother and father (his father was a plumber) would have been amazed if they had known how famous their son would one day become . . . and for what reason. Yuri Gargarin, too, the Russian flyer, was only born in 1934 (his father was a carpenter who could not read and write, and taught himself when he was grown up) and he was First Man into space in April, 1961 . . . So goodness knows where man will have arrived by next April . . . or where the Race into Space will end.

| YURI GAGARIN | ALAN B. SHEPHARD | VIRGIL I. GRISSOM | JOHN H. GLENN |

At the moment the USA and Russia seem to be in competition with each other: but in fact there is a suggestion that they will pool their resources. Then both countries will go ahead twice as fast.

This is how the Space Race looks in 1962

USA

1921 John Glenn born.

1924 Alan Shephard born.

1927 Virgil Grissom born.

1958 Jan 31. Explorer I 1,600 miles up.
March 17. Vanguard I 2,513 miles up.
March 26. Explorer III 1,735 miles.
July 26. Explorer IV 1,700 miles.
Oct 11. Pioneer I 79,000 miles.
Dec 6. Pioneer III 66,654 miles.
Dec 18. Atlas 8,750 miles.

1959 Feb 17. Vanguard II 2,050 miles.
Feb 28. Discoverer I 1,300 miles.
Mar 3. Pioneer IV solar orbit still there!

1961 March 25. Dummy launched in 'Redstone rocket'.
April 30. Dummy (sweating and breathing) launched in capsule Mercury had to be brought down.
May 6. Shephard flew 115 miles up in capsule, weight 30 tons, 300 miles over Atlantic.
July 22. Grissom 118 miles 303 miles over sea. Capsule sank.
Sept 14. Space capsule takes pictures.
Nov 30. Chimpanzee Enos in Mercury orbits twice.

1962 Feb 21. John Glenn does 3 orbits in Friendship VII.
May 24. Lieutenant Commander Malcolm Scott Carpenter orbited 3 times.

RUSSIA

1934 Yuri Gargarin born.

1957 Oct. First Sputnik 560 miles up.
Nov. Second Sputnik with dog 1,038 miles up.

1958 May. Third Sputnik ($2\frac{1}{2}$ tons) 150 miles up.
August. First stage rocket plus 2 dogs.

1959 Jan. Multistage Rocket Lunik I still in space!
July 2. 1 stage rocket, 2 dogs, 1 rabbit all safe.
Sept 12. Multistage rocket direct hit on moon . . . still there!
Oct 4. Multistage rocket Lunar III photographed far side of moon and sent pictures to earth.

1960 May 15. Space ship and dummy, $4\frac{1}{2}$ tons went into circular orbit but when firing forward, firing rockets mis-fired . . . so it's still there, circling in outer space.
Aug 19. First living creature (dog) to orbit earth and return.
Dec 1. Space Ship III plus 2 dogs destroyed when attempting re-entry into earth's atmosphere.

1961 Feb 12. Space Station I (1,420 lbs) launched from Sputnik orbiting earth on trajectory aimed at Venus.
April 12. Yuri Gargarin does single orbit of earth . . .

If you study these figures closely you will see that while the Russians were the first into space, the Americans have always been more certain of their manouvreing and re-entry into the earth's atmosphere . . . So nobody can yet be said to have won a lead over the other.

When will the first man land on the moon? It might even happen this year.

45

so you want to be a POP STAR

by CLIFF RICHARD

ALL you really need is that "Big Break". Let me tell you about mine!

I came to England from my birth place in Lucknow, India when I was eight. Ten years later I became established in show business and when I was twenty I was able to write my life story.

It all started while I was at Cheshunt Secondary Modern School; Bill Haley came to town and I played truant to see him rock 'n' roll. I lost my prefect badge the next day. I left school and became a clerk at the factory where my father worked, and was given an old five guinea guitar with which I joined a local skiffle group. However I quickly formed a group of my own and we were soon doing local dates.

In 1958 I entered the Carroll Levis audition at Shepherds Bush and clicked, thanks to the practice I had at a thousand amateur talent nights.

I was introduced to Norrie Paramor of Columbia records and we cut a disc originally intended as a flip side called "Move It," which eventually sold half a million.

Meanwhile I did a seasonal engagement at Billy Butlin's Clacton Holiday camp and did so well that I gave up my job at the radio factory.

When I appeared on Television's "Oh Boy" the producer Jack Good insisted that I removed my side burns and sang without plucking my guitar. "What will I do with my hands?" "Who'll recognise me without my side burns?" I asked, but I obeyed and was lucky.

By the time I was nineteen I had achieved six of my great ambitions, I had a number one record in the Hit Parade, I received a Golden Disc, "Livin' Doll", I had made two films, "Serious Charge" and "Expresso Bongo", I appeared at a Royal Command Performance, on Sunday Night at the London Palladium, and in the United States.

Since then things have gone full steam ahead, culminating last year with the highly successful musical "The Young Ones" and right now I am filming "Summer Holiday" on location in Greece.

My private life? I rarely have time for any really, but when I am at home I can gaze with satisfaction at my Thunder Bird sports car and my weekly allowance has been raised from ten pounds to fifteen pounds in order that I can run it. My only really extravagant taste is for expensive clothes and at home I have two wardrobes . . . one for suits and one for shirts.

How do I feel about fame? Well sometimes to be alone is marvellous but I'd hate to be unrecognised for any length of time.

Fame is wonderful but it's exhausting and materially it has brought certain luxuries like my car and house.

My fan club now numbers over twelve thousand, 95 per cent of which are girls but I don't intend to marry until I am twenty five at least. I could never be sure whether a girl wanted to date the Cliff Richard I am or the Harry Webb I was born.

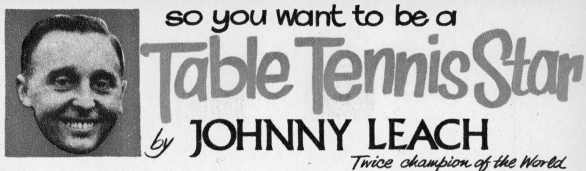

so you want to be a
Table Tennis Star
by JOHNNY LEACH
Twice champion of the World

WHATEVER game you decide to play, you should always play it with the idea of becoming the world champion. You may not succeed, but that isn't the point: in striving towards this peak of perfection you are bound to improve, and the better you can play the more you will enjoy the game.

For those few who are capable of winning top honours, Table Tennis offers particularly rich rewards in travel and friendship for there is scarcely one corner of this wide world where the muffled click of rubber bat against celluloid ball is not a familiar and inspiring sound.

Ours is a game which almost anyone can take part in simply by picking up a bat and copying what others are seen to be doing. Like most youngsters, I started by playing my Dad on the kitchen table at home. A word of warning here, though: as soon as possible you should find an opportunity to get some instruction on a full-sized table. The reason for this is that it is so easy for a novice to get into bad playing habits which later on become increasingly difficult to lose.

Youngsters today are lucky because every Butlin's Holiday Camp boasts the most up-to-date Table Tennis facilities with expert NEWS OF THE WORLD coaches ready to help everyone from beginner to potential champion.

To get to the top in Table Tennis today, good coaching is essential. Without seeking to interfere in any way with your natural ability an experienced teacher will show you the 'short cuts'—things that you won't have the time to discover by trial and error because Table Tennis is a game for young people and its champions are getting younger all the time.

For example, no matter how powerful your forehand drive may be it will not be of any service unless you are at the right place at the right time, and in the right position to use it. Good footwork which puts you in the correct sideways position to play each shot is the first essential, and it does not happen by accident — you need someone to show you how.

Take my tip then, if you want to be a star—learn the A.B.C. of the game from an established teacher first. The rest is up to you!

Yours in sport.
JOHNNY LEACH

BE A MAGICIAN

Trick A. The Vanishing and Re-appearing Coin.

Objects needed.

1 tumbler.
1 large sheet of white paper.
Another sheet of the same paper.
A pair of scissors.
Some good strong glue.
A sheet of newspaper.

This is a really fine magic feat. You will need a tumbler, a large sheet of white paper . . . another sheet of the same paper, a pair of scissors, some good glue and a sheet of newspaper.

Put some glue around the lip of the tumbler, turn it over and press it onto a sheet of white paper. When the glue has dried, cut the paper away from the outside of the glass figure (1). When this is done, make a cone out of the piece of newspaper big enough to cover the tumbler and all is ready.

Place the "special" tumbler upside down on the big sheet of white paper and beside it place a coin. Now announce that you will make the coin disappear and appear at will. Cover the tumbler with the cone of newspaper and move the tumbler on top of the coin. This will hide the fact that you have a disc of paper glued to the lip of the tumbler. Say Abracadabra . . . lift the cone away and the coin will have vanished . . . it is of course under the secret paper disc which is quite invisible. To bring the coin back just reverse the movements.

GLUE EDGE

FIGURE 1

Trick C. The Magic of Inertia.
Objects needed.

1 stiff loop of paper.

1 bottle, with neck large enough to admit a coin.

1 magic wand.

1 small coin.

Make this properly and you will win for yourself a reputation for great skill.

With glue and a strip of stiff paper make a loop which can be balanced on top of a bottle, which has a neck wide enough to allow a small coin to drop easily into it.

If you have all three things ready along with a stick or ruler, you can begin.

Balance ring and coin as in fig. 1.

Now with a great show of concentration hold your stick inside the loop and with a flick knock the ring away from under the coin . . . if you have arranged everything well the coin will fall into the bottle (fig. 2).

The secret is to see that the coin is placed exactly right, and that you give the paper loop a really sharp flick and the law of Inertia will do the rest.

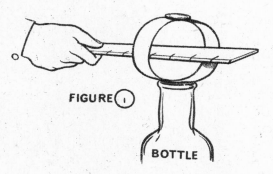

FIGURE ①

BOTTLE

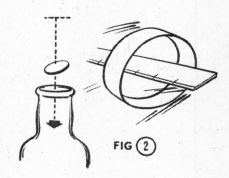

FIG ②

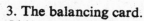

3. The balancing card.
Objects needed.

1 card.

1 match.

For this trick you will need a playing card and a match and plenty of practice.

Hold the card and the match as shown in fig. 2. Put your right hand back upwards under the card and rest the card upon it.

Slide the match downwards until it can be gripped between the fingers of the right hand, let the card rest against the match and take your left hand away. To the viewers it will appear to be balanced.

Now reverse the movements . . . grip the card and match with the left hand, and with the left thumb move the match upwards and when it is clear of the edge of the card lift it from the right hand. Now with the right hand take the card away from the left leaving the match in the left hand.

Hand the card to someone else to try . . . but never tell anyone about the match in your left hand . . . just get rid of it as soon as you can.

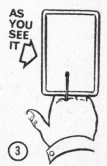

AS YOU SEE IT ⇨

③

THE MAGIC HANDKERCHIEF

Trick B. The Magic Handkerchief.
Objects needed.
1 handkerchief (clean, but you can borrow it).
2 lots of cheek and good 'patter'.

This trick is lots of fun . . . especially when you have a party. Invite someone from your audience to help you, and explain that you are about to make a handkerchief disappear under the most difficult conditions . . . and what is more you will borrow the handkerchief.

Have your friend sit comfortably on a chair with his hands on his lap. You take up your position in front of your helper so that if you were to reach out you could touch the top of his head. Hold the handkerchief between your hands at arms length . . . and with a sweeping up and down movement wave the handkerchief in front of the helper. Ask him to look right into your eyes and to concentrate. As you sweep your arms up and down in a continuous movement slowly gather the handkerchief up into your hands until it vanishes from sight . . . NOW . . . without interrupting the smooth movement of your arms release the handkerchief just as the hands reach the point above your friend's head . . . the handkerchief will fly over his head and drop silently behind him . . . carry on moving your arms and then stop . . . open your hands and show that the hankie has gone . . . the assistant will be dumbfounded . . . YOU MUST PRACTICE THIS.

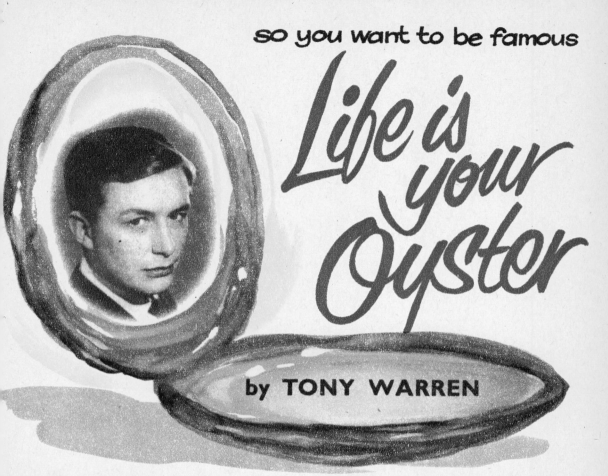

so you want to be famous

Life is your Oyster

by TONY WARREN

HAVE you ever imagined yourself descending from an airliner in a blaze of photographers flash-lights with reporters screaming for statements? Of course you have.

I've even done it. The only thing was that the cameras and the notebooks weren't waiting for me, they were all for a friend of mine, somewhere one step higher, just behind my left shoulder blade.

He's famous, I'm not.

I may be the writer of a top television serial but no-one knows what I look like . . . thank goodness!

If you're Adam Faith you've only to set foot on the pavement for a dozen heads to swivel rigid. It doesn't just stop at staring. People come right up and burst into lengthy conversation.

"Of *course* I like talking to all sorts of different people" says Adam. "Who doesn't? But it can be a bit awkward if you're rushing off to keep an urgent appointment or you're not feeling particularly chatty. You've always got to remember, though, that this may be the only time these people'll ever see you and if you seem the slightest bit snooty—even if you don't mean to—they'll soon pass the word round."

Patricia Phoenix, *Coronation Street*'s Elsie Tanner, says: "People in the street honestly believe they *know* me. It's not surprising really, after all I whizz across the home screens, in their own living rooms, twice-weekly at seven thirty! To them I don't exist, I'm just Elsie Tanner and when they see me out shopping in my mink I can see them whispering and wondering just where

51

Ma. Tanner got *that*."

Of course, if you're famous, you can always resort to disguise but there's something rather noticeable about false side-whiskers and you and I would look decidedly odd in dark glasses in the middle of November.

Most autograph hunters are polite and well behaved but there are of course, others who probably, because they are excited, forget to say 'please' and 'thank you' and those who say; "What rotten writing" should try signing their signature, with a borrowed pen, on a scrappy bit of paper held up against the wall.

Have you ever written a fan letter and then got annoyed because you've had to wait ages for an answer? Well I do ask you to have a little patience because your favourite Star is really a hardworking person.

Many people write to me about my television programmes and I love hearing from them. Some of the letters are warm and friendly and others plain abusive. I've got one, in which an anonymous gent actually threatened me because he disapproved of an episode in Coronation Street—framed on my bedroom wall. If there's an address, all these letters get answered . . . In time. When you're working at television pressure there just aren't enough hours in the day so it's quite often weeks before correspondence gets answered. It is difficult for some people to understand this and on occasions a second letter zooms through the letter box chasing up the first one.

If you're in the public eye — and you want to stay there — you need co-operative publicity and plenty of it. At first you'll be excited at being interviewed by Newspapermen but — as the thrill wears off — you'll come to realise that you're totally at the mercy of some, not many thank heavens — reporters. They put words into your mouth that you never even realised you knew and in the end you finish up as a ventriloquist's dummy while your Agent does all the talking.

Recently I met Violet Carson, television's Ena Sharples coming out of the Studios, glowering into a newspaper. She looked as though she was capable of starting a paper chase with the thing she read aloud; "Miss Carson has found fame in the twilight of her life."

"If that's fame" snorted my stormy Leading Lady, "it's downright impertinent and I'm going home to grow roses!"

With this she tucked the paper under her

arm and dived smartly into a taxi as a dozen Middle aged ladies, armed with shopping bags, charged her with cries of "It's Ena!"

And does fame bring a whole host of new friends? No. To have friends, and keep them, you need time for letters and telephone calls and dates and what I believe Queen Victoria used to call 'The Theatre and the Dance.' The Theatre and the Dance? Huh! If you've time for a quick cuppa, once every other February, with your nearest and dearest, you'll be doing well. As Cliff Richard puts it; "It's not that you lose your friends but they mostly work during the day. I work at night. If we *could* get together, I'm sure we'd have a ball but it's just a question of when."

If you're lucky enough to have watched Helen Shapiro taking her bow to tremendous cheers at the London Palladium you probably imagined that, off-stage, she leads just such another glamorous, glamorous life. Poor old misguided you!

You know what Helen told me just a few days ago as we waited for her Manager just inside the stage-door?

"A couple of weeks back, I had a night

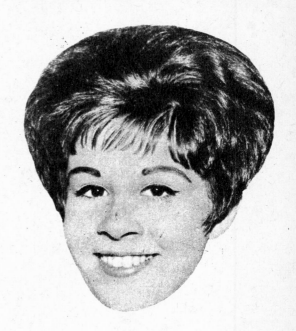

off and my cousin and I went back for the evening to my old youth club. It was great."

This wasn't the Big Star trying to sound Simple and Untouched by Success, it was Helen telling the bald truth.

Your life is, in all probability far more exciting than Adam's or Cliff's or Helen's or all the film stars and television personalities and model girls put together. Why? You've got time to enjoy yourself, they haven't. They're well known because they work. It's as simple as that. And if they're to stay where they are, at the top, they've got to keep right on working.

Do you still fancy yourself as one of the Famous?

This morning, a photographer came round to my flat to take the picture at the beginning of this article. While he was setting up his lights the telephone rang. It was a journalist. Could he come round and interview me?

I've been asked for my autograph, admittedly only three times in seven weeks. But you must admit it's a start.

Because — for all I've said against it — *I* do want to be famous.

FOUR ALARM FIZZLE

FRED! THERE GOES THE FIRE ALARM BIRD, AND YOU'RE A VOLUNTEER FIREMAN!

WAUK! WAUK! WAUK!

OKAY, OKAY... CALM DOWN, EVERYBODY!

NOW, WHERE'S THE FIRE, YOU BIG BLABBER-BILLED ALARMIST?

WAUK! WAUK!

WE'LL MAKE SHORT WORK OF THAT BLAZE, EH, FRED?

YEAH!

COME ON... LET'S GET OUR EXTINGUISHER!

FIRE HOSE HOUSE

GIDDYUP, ELFY!

NOW WE'D BETTER GET RELOADED FOR THE **NEXT** FIRE...CAN'T HOPE TO BLOW 'EM ALL OUT!

YEAH! OUR HOSE MIGHT THROW ITS NOSE OUT OF JOINT!

SAY, I'LL **NEVER** GET BACK TO MY HAMMOCK AT THIS RATE...

UNLESS I CATCH THAT FIREBUG AND STOP HIM FROM SETTING ANY MORE TREES ABLAZE!

YIKES! HE'S ABOUT TO TOUCH OFF ANOTHER ONE NOW!

BITE THE DIRT, YOU FIREBUG, YOU!

HUH? FIREBUG?

HOW **DARE** YOU! I'M BEARING THE TORCH FROM MOUNT BLOW-TORCH TO LIGHT THE BIG BONFIRE AT THE OLYMPIC GROUNDS!

THEY'RE ALL WAITING FOR THIS TO SIGNAL THE START OF THE OLYMPIC GAMES!

PARDON ME! THE GAMES MUST GO ON, I GUESS!

BUT Y-YOU'RE SETTING PALMS ABLAZE!

OH, QUIET! IT'S MY FEET THAT FEEL LIKE THEY'RE AFIRE!

57

The End

THE FLINTSTONES

TOLL CROSSING

DUCK DIVING . . . That's the way to begin. First duck your head under, as you swim along on the surface. Get accustomed to breathing out, gently and *slowly* through your nose, as you swim along. Having your eyes *open* is terribly interesting, and the world looks quite different down there in the blue, blue depths. Now you should be ready for the dive.

Get into chest high water. Rise to toes. Spring off. Point arms downwards and hitch your hips over your head. You'll *shoot* down — so watch it. Now point your hands up, and raise your head slightly . . . and you'll rise to the surface. Do it again and again until you're confident with it.

Under Water Swimming: why not, now you can duck dive? Swim forwards on the surface, and when you feel good and ready take a deep breath and drop arms and head downwards. Make a powerful breast stroke, pulling you under. Bend in the middle and flick your legs upwards. This gives that added push to your downward movement. Your first plunge will carry you a good ten feet, so don't scrabble with further strokes. Let the air gently out of your lungs and swim slowly, breast stroke with your legs. But you can paddle if you're wearing flippers and then you fairly shoot along.
Somersault.

Now you should be ready for water tricks!

Start as for under water swimming, but draw knees up to stomach and tuck your legs in. Keep your head on your tummy and go on making steady paddle movements with your hands. So long as you breath quickly as you come up to the surface of the water you can go on as long as you like, going over and over like a ball . . .
Backward Somersault.

Float on your back, then fling your head backwards and downwards. Blow through your nose, if the water worries you! Bring your arms out of the water and down and sweep them *up* towards the surface in a powerful paddle movement, at the same time tuck your knees well up.

The great thing with water is to feel at home in it — so don't try these tricks until you feel secure.

WATER SAFETY CODE

1. Avoid taking risks, or overestimating your ability.
2. Avoid swimming alone—safety in numbers.
3. Beware of big waves.
4. Take care when chasing beach balls etc, carried out by the tide.
5. Avoid diving until you are sure the water is deep enough — and there are no hidden rocks or obstructions.
6. Avoid diving into swift flowing rivers.
7. Avoid swimming where there are weeds.
8. Never race out to a buoy — tides and currents may change for the swim home . . .
9. Never call 'help' in fun.
10. Learn artificial respiration.

Underwater Wisdom

1. Never dive alone: when wearing a mask and breathing tube it is easy to travel out of help.
2. Never walk about with a loaded harpoon gun.
3. Always unload before leaving the water.
4. Never point a harpoon gun at anyone.
5. Never use an aqua lung or any other water breathing apparatus until you have been properly trained and have passed the recognised tests.
6. Never use such apparatus on your own. Always swim with others and have a boat standing by if possible.
7. Use only approved equipment.

THE ART OF GIVING

by

TOM PUGH

Senior Chaplain, Butlins Holiday Camps

My Dear Beavers,

I was so happy when Miss Spain asked me to write a short message on the art of giving, and I found myself thinking of that small boy on that far away mountain top when our Lord Jesus performed the wonderful Miracle of feeding the five thousand. You will all remember when, as dusk was falling and thousands of people were a long distance from home, our Lord asked his Disciples to give the multitude something to eat, to which they replied "how can this be possible when we are so far away from any City?" When he enquired of them what food they did have, he was told of the small boy who was carrying a picnic basket containing five loaves and two fishes, who was willing to give his basket of food for the good of all. The Lord Blessed the gift and thus all the people were satisfied through the kindness and foresight of the boy.

I tell you this because the boy knew that some people could be fed, so that he had brought to the Meeting all that he possessed in the way of food, which enabled the Miracle to be performed. He was the right type of boy, who was in the right place at the right time, with the right feelings.

I am sure there are many times when your parents call you and you are not there, or if you are there you are not always equipped to help them and, you know that the person who suffers most for this fault is not the parent but the person who has failed to carry out his mission. The best way for you to get satisfaction is by giving service to others, and this is particularly true of boys and girls on holiday. I ask you to remember that your holiday is also your parents' holiday, and if you remember this you will find that you not only make their holiday happy, but you will give your own self a wonderful lasting satisfaction.

I wish you all a very happy holiday always and look forward to seeing you on one of our Camps.

so you want to be a ...
T.V. PRODUCER

The thrilling know-how of the world behind Your Favourite Programmes Described by ace producer
HARRY CARLISLE
of the BBC and of Juke Box Jury

STARTING a T.V. programme is rather like launching a rocket to the moon. With his eyes glued to the second hand of the Control Gallery clock the Producer starts to 'Count down' the seconds — 10 . 9 . 8 . 7 . 6 . 5 . 4 . 3 . 2 . 1 — Fade UP!

It is on the command 'Fade Up' that everything really starts. The Vision Mixer, who sits next to the Producer in the Control Gallery, has an array of buttons and levers in front of him. Each lever or button controlling a camera.

When the Producer says "Fade Up

Camera 1" the Vision Mixer pushes forward the lever marked Camera 1. Slowly the scene that Camera 1 is looking at on the Studio floor will appear on the Master Transmission screen in the Control Gallery. It will of course also appear on your sets at home.

In front of the Producer's seat in the gallery there are a lot of television sets which we call monitors.

Sometimes in the big studios there are as many as nine of these monitors. The simplest way to explain how we use the monitors is to think of them as "camera viewfinders." In other words the monitor labelled No. 1 is showing the Producer the scene or view at which Camera 1 is looking. Monitor No. 2 is showing the scene at which camera 2 is looking. And so on . . .

If the Producer has 'Faded Up' Camera 1 (so that viewers at home are watching the scene being photographed by Camera 1), and he then decides that he wants to change to the scene being photographed by Camera 2—he simply says "Cut to Camera 2." The Vision Mixer presses the button marked "Camera 2" and the picture automatically changes.

Four cameras

Normally a Producer uses four cameras in a television show. You will easily understand that using 4 cameras means that the Producer could be photographing the same scene from four different angles. By cutting from one camera to another he can show the viewers whichever angle of the scene he thinks most effective.

The Vision Mixer and the Producer control the picture side of the programme. The Vision Mixer is a very important member of the television production crew.

Another important member of the crew is the Sound Supervisor. All pictures have to be accompanied by sound. The Sound Supervisor has his own control panel in a different part of the Control Gallery. His job is like a Vision Mixer in some ways. But instead of cutting or mixing between cameras, a Sound Supervisor cuts and mixes between microphones.

In a show like the Black and White Minstrels the Sound Supervisor has to control about 30 microphones.

Let me give you an example.

When Juke Box Jury starts, you hear the familiar tune 'Hit or Miss' playing quite loudly. After a few bars the Sound Supervisor makes it play more quietly. At the same time 'fades up' the microphone in front of David Jacobs. In this way you can hear David talking quite clearly. If the Sound man did not do this all you would hear would be a jumble of noise.

So far we have spoken about the Sound and Vision side of a television show. We must not forget lighting. This is most important. Any of you who own a camera will know that to take a good photograph you must stand in the right position in relation to the sun. Or if you are doing indoor photography you must use a flash or put your lights in the best possible positions to improve your composition.

On a Television Show there is always a Lighting Supervisor. He arranges the lights so that the cameras take good clear pictures, which are also artistic. This point about the artistic pictures is important. In fact, every member of a television production crew has to be two things — An engineer (in either the sound or light field) and quite an artist as well!

The lights used in a television Studio are different from those you use in home photography of course. We do use some quite small lamps called 'inky dinks' which are only 200 watts. We use 500 watt lamps which are called 'pups'. But mostly we use big 2 kilowatt and 5 kilowatt lamps. On very rare occasions we even employ 10 kilowatt lamps. Then there are the very powerful arc lamps of 150 amps, and even one of 250 amps which is called 'a brute'.

Those of you who have studied the subject of "Light" in your school physics courses will soon realise that such lamps put out a lot of heat (as well as a lot of light).

This is one of the main unpleasantnesses in studio work. In spite of air conditioning the studios are always very hot.

Heat of course causes "perspiration". Perspiration plays havoc with make-up. So this is why, whenever an artist is not actually being photographed in a scene, but is let's say, waiting to play a later scene, the make-up girls dash up with their chamois leathers and mop the artist's brow and touch up his make up.

I am sure that now and again you have occasionally heard a strange clatter or bang that you obviously were not intended to hear? This usually means that something has fallen down in the studio—it is usually one of the wooden supports called "braces" which are used to hold up the scenery.

Hard work

I mention this because it is not generally realised that quite often during a television show a whole set of scenery has to be taken down or 'struck' and another scene put up or 'set'.

This is done whilst another part of the studio is actually being photographed—but it has to be done in complete silence.

People often think that working in television is very glamorous. So it is. But it is also very hard work and sometimes not at all glamorous. For instance, a show like Z Cars has to be rehearsed for a *week* before the cast are ready to move into the studio. Then in one day they do the show before the cameras.

These rehearsals (which are very tiring indeed) are usually done in cold, rather dreary empty halls all over London. Usually they are in places where it is difficult to get a decent meal—not a bit glamorous.

I am often asked what is the difference between a Television Producer and a Television Director. This is difficult to answer. A Television Producer is a man (or woman) in overall charge of the show — be it a play or a Musical. He is responsible for the entire programme. He has to satisfy himself that he has a good script, a good cast to play

the script, the right cameras, microphones, lights and what-have-you to do the job properly—And he must only spend a certain amount of money (called his budget) in doing all this. Normally a Producer also rehearses the artists in the piece. He then takes his cast into the studio and does the "camera direction" required to turn it into a Television programme.

Sometimes however a Producer will use a Director to do this last part of the job. The rehearsal of the cast in an outside rehearsal room and then the camera direction in the studio. Producers and Directors have to work in complete harmony. You can imagine this calls for a great deal of tact and patience on both sides!

What advice would I give to those of you who want to become Television Producers? Well I liked English Literature and History at school and I was good at them — both have been useful. I belonged to my School Dramatic Society and the Debating Society — and this experience turned out very useful as well. I tried to go to the right sort of films, plays and shows and most important of all I tried to learn something from all that I saw.

I wish now that I had been a bit brighter at Physics — it's useful to know the principals of heat, light and sound and if you don't learn them at school you'll have to learn them later. The great thing is to train yourself to *look* at things so that your eye takes in all the detail. When you are looking at something you should walk round it and try and decide which is the most attractive viewpoint or angle.

Finally before you can become a Television Producer you will need some practical experience in acting or producing. This is best obtained in either the film or theatre worlds in some humble capacity. In this way you can benefit from the experience of others.

Later on you should switch to television. Then you can apply your own experience to the special and very exciting field of television.

so you want to be a

RACING DRIVER

by Sheila Van Damm

WELL, you start as soon as you can walk! Every time you're out you learn a little more road sense. You watch the traffic lights, watch what the cars are doing, learn to tell the good drivers. When you're with your parents in the car you learn still more. Look a long way ahead and try and decide what the various cars are going to do (this is something that will one day be very important to you on the race track).

As soon as possible, learn to ride a bicycle, and learn to ride it really well. Study the Highway Code until you know it inside out, and go in for all the proficiency and safety awards you can. (By the way, Prince Charles was this year given the Award for Safer Cycling, having ridden safely for a year after taking his National Cycling Proficiency Test). To be a racing driver you must be really good, so never miss a chance to learn a bit more. Keep your bicycle in tip-top condition always, and try and understand exactly how it works. Every racing driver has to know a very great deal about his car and what he can ask of it at high speeds.

Later on you'll find all this experience helps you enormously when you start learning to drive a car. Save up for proper lessons with a good school, and don't try and get friends or family to teach you. (You might learn bad habits!) From then on you need lots of experience — thousands of miles of it. You'll probably join a local Car Club. You'll go on learning, taking more and more advanced tests, getting surer and wiser and safer. And then one day you'll find you are sitting in a small open car, a crash helmet lashed on your head, and your foot on the throttle of a powerful car which is pointed along a racing circuit. Back in the control room a real expert will be watching you to see how you behave. To see whether you are just another of the wild ones, or whether you really have that fine balance of skill and courage and timing that is going to carry you into the Stirling Moss class. All the great speed merchants, Phil Hill, John Surtees, Graham Hill, Jack Brabham, Donald Campbell etc, all began just like you.

Learning the Highway Code.

PIXIE, DIXIE and MR. JINKS
SOMETHING FISHY

SPORTING RECORDS

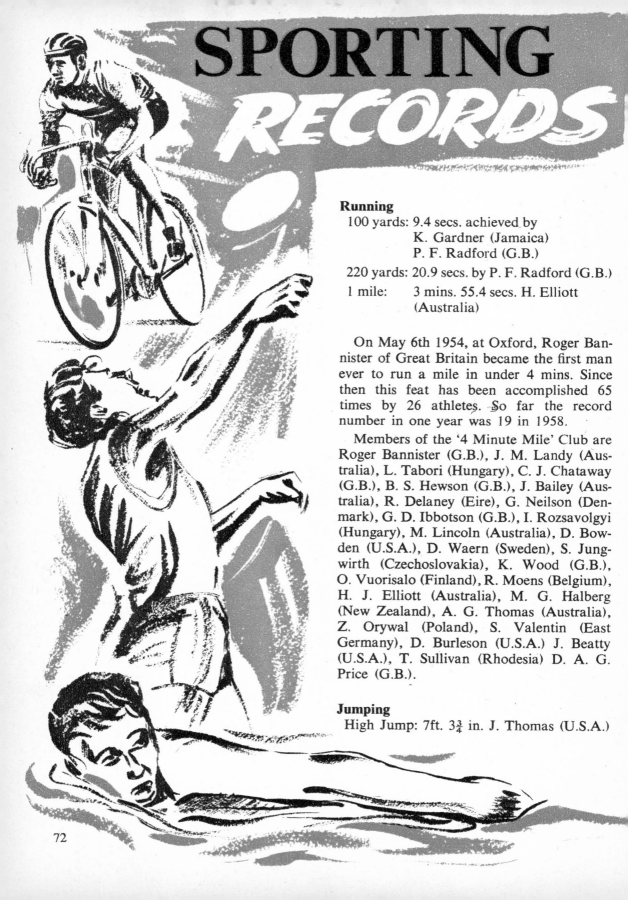

Running

100 yards: 9.4 secs. achieved by
           K. Gardner (Jamaica)
           P. F. Radford (G.B.)

220 yards: 20.9 secs. by P. F. Radford (G.B.)

1 mile: 3 mins. 55.4 secs. H. Elliott
           (Australia)

On May 6th 1954, at Oxford, Roger Bannister of Great Britain became the first man ever to run a mile in under 4 mins. Since then this feat has been accomplished 65 times by 26 athletes. So far the record number in one year was 19 in 1958.

Members of the '4 Minute Mile' Club are Roger Bannister (G.B.), J. M. Landy (Australia), L. Tabori (Hungary), C. J. Chataway (G.B.), B. S. Hewson (G.B.), J. Bailey (Australia), R. Delaney (Eire), G. Neilson (Denmark), G. D. Ibbotson (G.B.), I. Rozsavolgyi (Hungary), M. Lincoln (Australia), D. Bowden (U.S.A.), D. Waern (Sweden), S. Jungwirth (Czechoslovakia), K. Wood (G.B.), O. Vuorisalo (Finland), R. Moens (Belgium), H. J. Elliott (Australia), M. G. Halberg (New Zealand), A. G. Thomas (Australia), Z. Orywal (Poland), S. Valentin (East Germany), D. Burleson (U.S.A.) J. Beatty (U.S.A.), T. Sullivan (Rhodesia) D. A. G. Price (G.B.).

Jumping

High Jump: 7ft. 3¾ in. J. Thomas (U.S.A.)

Pole Vault: 15 ft. 9$\frac{1}{4}$ in. D. Bragg (U.S.A.)
Long Jump: 26 ft. 8$\frac{1}{4}$ in. J. C. Owens
    (U.S.A.)
            26 ft. 11$\frac{1}{4}$ in. R. Boston (U.S.A.)
            (awaits ratification)

Throwing
  Discus: 196 ft. 6$\frac{1}{2}$ in. E. Piatkowski (Poland)
  Shot: 65 ft. 7 in. W. H. Nieder (USA)
  Hammer: 225 ft. 4 in. H. V. Connolly (USA)
  Javelin: 282 ft. 3$\frac{1}{2}$ in. A. Cantello (USA)

Cycling
1,000 miles: Eileen Sheridan (G.B.)
Land's End to John o' Groats: E. Sheridan
    (G.B.)

Motor Racing
  1 Mile: Sir John Cobb 403.135 unratified
          394.196 m.p.h.

Swimming—Free Style
  100 metres: J. Devitt (Australia)
              54.6 secs.
  200 metres: T. Yamasaka (Japan)
              2 mins. 1.5 secs.
  220 yards: J. Konrads (Australia)
              2 mins. 1.6 secs.
  400 metres: J. Konrads (Australia)
              4 mins. 15.9 secs.
  440 yards: J. Konrads (Australia)
              4 mins. 15.9 secs.
  800 metres: J. Konrads (Australia)
              8 mins. 59.6 secs.
  880 yards: J. Konrads (Australia)
              8 mins. 59.6 secs.
1,500 metres: J. Konrads (Australia)
              17 mins. 11.0 secs.

PARTY Time

4-6 YEAR-OLDS.

Why not have a PARTY all by yourself?

Why not colour the holiday pictures on pages 14 and 15.

Done that? Get Mummy to draw some big squiggles for you on a sheet of paper . . . It is easy to make a snake out of a curly squiggle but see if you can make a tent . . . or a clown out of the letter A.

Are you near a kitchen? Does mummy keep empty jam jars? Ask her to lend you eight . . . Fill them with water, different levels in each. Now tap them (gently) with a pencil . . . They can play a tune and if you take care in filling them from the tap you can get all the notes in the scale.

6-12 YEAR-OLDS.

Get your friends to play this game with you.

Cover the floor with buttons from mummy's box, some near to you . . . and some far away.

Now get a hat, an *old* hat is best, and see if you can throw the hat to cover the buttons one by one, taking turns. The boy or girl who covers the most buttons wins.

Find your twin! Mummy will tell you secretly in whispers to hop, jump, skip, shrug your shoulders, snap your fingers, or even crawl. When she says 'Go' start doing the thing she told you . . . look around and pair yourself off with the person doing the same movement as yourself *quick as you can*. The boy or girl who is *last* pays a forfeit.

A good idea is to make him/her spell everyone's first name backwards!

TEEN-AGE PARTIES are lots of fun . . . but sometimes there is an awkward bit at the beginning when you stand around in groups, boys on one side, girls on the other and don't know how to get the party going . . .

Fun and Games

A good ice breaker . . .

Tell your pals to bring snaps of themselves as babies or as tiny tots and put them in a bowl. Pull them out one at a time and see if you can guess who each one is . . .

Another :

Stand in two lines, teams.

Boy, girl, boy, girl.

Now try to pass an orange quickly down the line from chin to chin, without touching the orange with your hands or any other part of you.

If you're not talking yet you must be a sticky lot . . .

Get them to guess how many times they can fold a sheet of newspaper. They'll guess 15, 20 . . . but they will find it impossible to fold more than six or seven times.

LEGS is a great game. The leader calls out the number of legs of a living creature . . . and the party has to shout out quickly the name of a creature . . . The leader might cry 'Four' and the answer might be 'Dog'.

Or 'None' and the answer might be 'Haddock' or 'Kipper'.

FINALLY, DO YOU KNOW THESE TWO NEW DROODLES ?

IN THIS BIRDCAGE WHICH ONE HAS BEEN PAID FOR ? ANSWER :- THE BOTTOM ONE, THE REST ARE ON THE HIGHER PURCHASE !

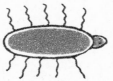

A WEEVIL

BUT WHAT IS THIS ?

ANS :- THE LESSER OF TWO WEEVILS.